BALD

ISBN-10: 0997977302

ISBN-13: 978-0997977301

Dear Oletta,

For families dealing with chronic and terminal illness

and for Lorin

Best Wishes!
Erica Hammar

BALD

Erica Hammon

When I grow up I'm going to be just like my big brother. He's super cool!

My brother wasn't feeling well so he went to the doctor. They found a big lump called a tumor growing inside of him.

What to do when you find out your brother has cancer:

- **Run to the top of the slide and yell, "PLEASE MAKE MY BIG BROTHER BETTER!"**
- **Cry as loud as you want**
- **Hug your favorite toy**

He stayed in the hospital for what seemed like a hundred days. Doctors did tons of stuff, like listening to his heart, testing his blood, and giving him shots. *OUCH!*

What to do when you miss a big brother:

- **Make cards with pets, puppies, and pirates**
- **Have skype time on the computer**
- **Take care of his tarantula**

"Please bring him home!" I begged Dad every day, and finally, he did.

How to welcome a big brother home:

- **Paint a HUGE sign with stars and smiley faces**
- **Give him a big, but *gentle* hug**
- **Surprise him with a present (like a spider jar or your favorite blankie)**

"Will you play catch with me?" I asked him after he came home.

"I'm so tired," he whispered.

How to play with a brother with *NO energy*:

- **Lay with him under the stars**
- **Make a blanket-tent to read under**
- **Show him your latest ninja moves**

Dad, Mom, and my brother decided the tumor needed to be taken out. The doctors put him to sleep with gas so it wouldn't hurt.

After surgery, brother had to have chemo treatments, which was supposed to make him better . . . Nope! It made him worse.

Mom said, "The medicine is working to get rid of the cancer."

How to take care of a brother during chemo:

- Wash your hands--use *lots* of soap
- Guard him from wild animals that may have germs
- Make sure he rests--SSSHHH!

Big brother doesn't like food anymore because chemo makes his tummy sick. So I tried feeding him some of his favorite foods.

What to feed a big brother who *doesn't want to eat*:

- **Ice cream or popsicles**
- **Warm Chicken Broth**
- **Pizza of course**

My brother is getting tired of cancer. He always says, "Don't act like I'm sick. Just act normal!"

How to act *normal* with a sick brother:

- **Sneak in the candy jar on top of his dresser**
- **Tell him NO when he asks you to do something (then do it anyway)**
- **Try on his cool hats and sunglasses and make silly faces at him**

The doctors said that chemo would make my brother's hair fall out. I could tell he was trying to be brave.   So, I had an idea . . . "Cha-Ching!" Have a head-shaving party, and shave my hair off too!

"Only shave the top first," I told mom. Then I borrowed dad's glasses and slid them down my nose.

"You look just like a little old man," brother chuckled, patting my bald spot.

The party was awesome! We all looked . . . well . . . *BALD*! Big brother smiled the whole time.

Mom was laughing so hard she was crying, "Bald is beautiful!"

How to have a *happy* head-shaving party:

- **Invite a bunch of friends (make sure they wash)**
- **Order big brother's favorite pizza**
- **Take lots of pictures**

It seemed like my brother was always sick. Then finally one day the doctors said the cancer was gone!   Hooray!

What to do when a big brother is well:

- **Run to the top of the slide and yell, "THANK YOU FOR MAKING MY BIG BROTHER BETTER!"**
- **Smile as big as you want**
- **Hug your favorite brother**
- **And . . . be as *brave* as he is.**

Author's Note

BALD is based on the true story of Lorin, who was diagnosed with stage four liver cancer at the age of fifteen. Lorin was young, healthy, and full of life. All that changed. It was difficult to watch, especially for a little brother who always looked up to Lorin.

Siblings of a person with cancer often feel fear, anger, and anxiety. Being a parent and watching with heart-wrenching anxiety is an experience challenging to describe. One has to remain firm in supporting them through the hard process, yet gentle and encouraging. Everyone is affected. The important thing is to stick together.

Although, there were many not-so-good times during Lorin's diagnosis and treatment, this story highlights the times that were good. The whole family cared for him in every way possible with love and support, GoFundMe pages, and pizza of course.

When the time came that Lorin's hair was going to fall out, they did, in-fact, invite a bunch of friends over for a *happy* head-shaving party with some "only shaving the top at first," even a little brother.

Bald is beautiful when you think of the courage it takes to fight cancer. My very best wishes to every brave soul who faces this disease. Warmest regards for you!   E.H.

Acknowledgements:

Thanks to Mike Patch and Geoff Griffin in this process, and to my Dad and Mom

for their support and encouragement through my health issues.

About the Author

Erica Hammon teaches special education students in Salt Lake City.

She enjoys the outdoors, gardening, singing out loud while driving, painting, and

volunteering at events for children. Having dealt with many challenges herself,

her goal is to help people of all ages to overcome their hurdles

and be successful. She enjoys writing articles and books that

inspire people to go beyond what they think possible.

"Whatever the mind can conceive . . . it can achieve." - Napoleon Hill

Other Books: **Top Ten Strategies for Student Engagement**

https://www.facebook.com/LookListenandLearn/

https://twitter.com/ehammon100

Made in the USA
San Bernardino, CA
17 September 2016